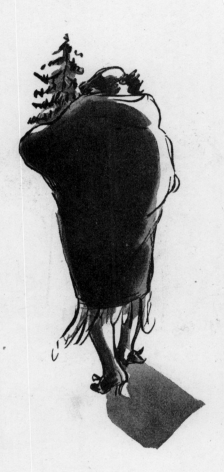

When Were *You* Built?

"When were *you* built?"

"I just want to say that I'm perfectly willing to serve as treasurer, provided every penny doesn't have to come out exactly even."

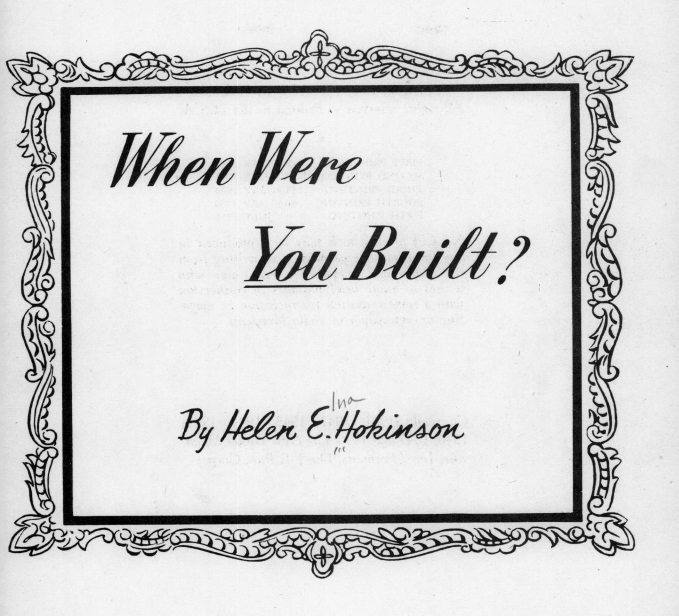

When Were You Built?

By Helen E. Hokinson

Ina

E. P. Dutton & Company, Inc.
New York

Lithographed by NEW YORK LITHOGRAPHING CORP.

To
JAMES REID PARKER

whose captions have inspired most
of these drawings.

Acknowledgment is made to *The New Yorker,* in which all of the drawings in this book originally appeared.

"I often wish I had kept up my mandolin lessons."

"I suppose I ought to gi
Stumpp & Walter som
of the credit."

"I never know how
far away to stand to make
them look good."

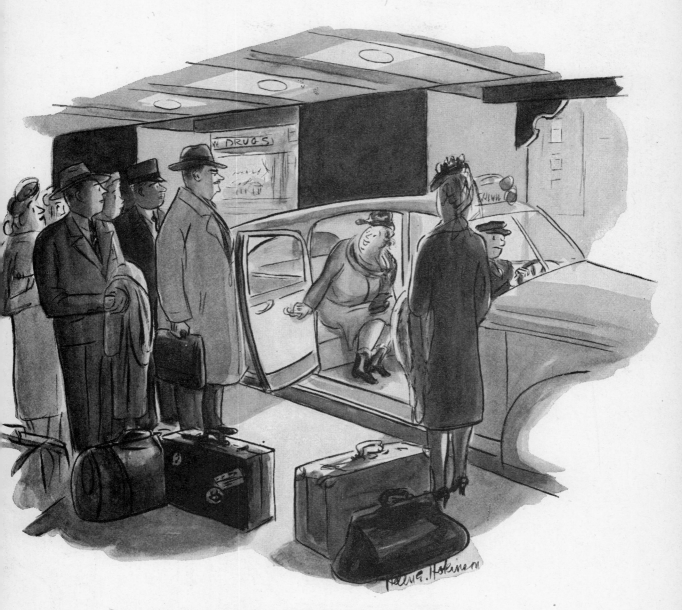

"Anyone else going to the Martha Washington?"

"I never give _my_ roses stimulants."

"I like poetry, all right
but I hate to pay five cents a day for it.

"Is it all right for an expectant mother to catch chipmunks?"

"But there are only seven more treatments in the course, Mrs. Freeman. We mustn't throw in the sponge now!"

"I've decided to give
Louis Bromfield another chance."

"But _why_ isn't a major fish, flesh, fowl, or good red herring, dear?"

"Now, don't worry, dear. I'm hoping I won't see anything I like."

"Now, the first thing we must ask ourselves is 'Why is the gazelle supple?'"

"Does it matter which end we do them from?"

"Excuse me. Do you happen to know what a porcupine symbolizes?"

"It's an allegory. You have to be feeling unreal to enjoy it."

"Of course, you'd have to have a castle or something."

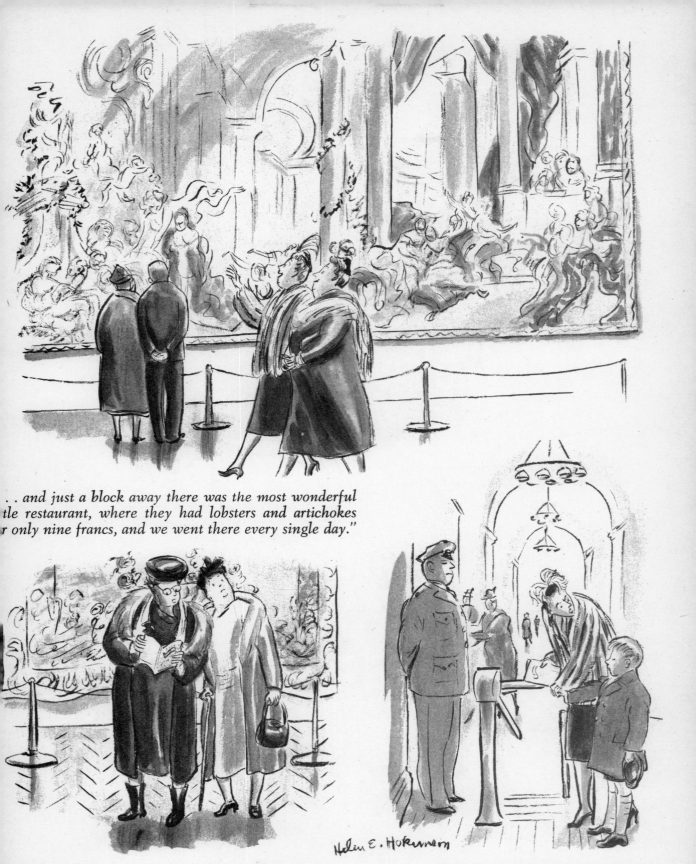

"... and just a block away there was the most wonderful ttle restaurant, where they had lobsters and artichokes r only nine francs, and we went there every single day."

Helen E. Hokinson

'Aurora, seated on a cloud with a cupid who olds a torch, looks down at Cephalus, who . . .' "

"Can't you remember anything but the blood that ran out of the horse?"

"Would this be all right for
a friend who isn't interested in much of anything?"

". . . and the little flower pocket definitely takes it out of the kitchen."

"*Well, if your husband isn't going to be at Hot Springs, either, we can get in all sorts of mischief.*"

"Now don't be timid. George tells me the Yale Club __wants__ women."

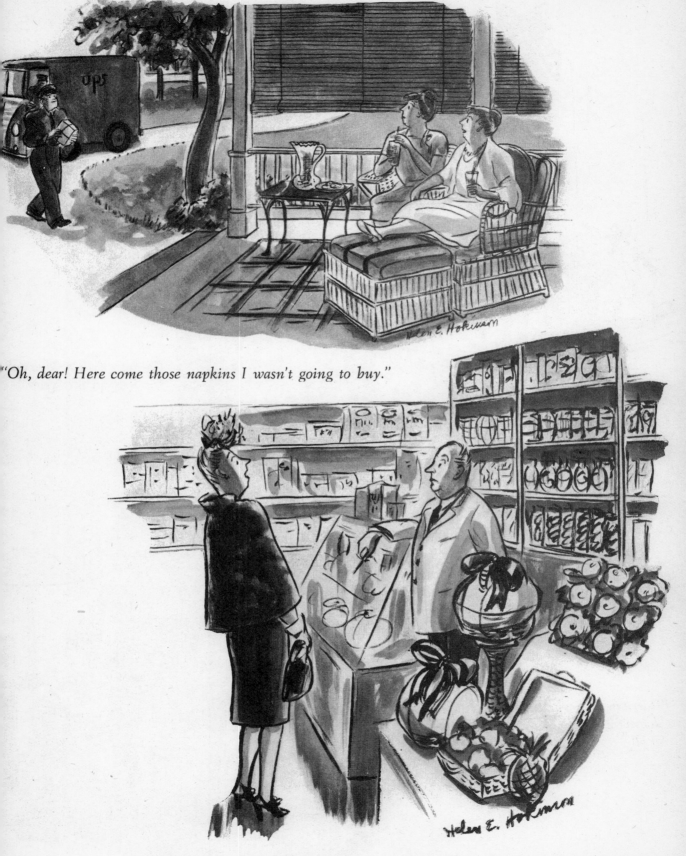

"Oh, dear! Here come those napkins I wasn't going to buy."

"You mean we still haven't conquered that place where my tea comes from?"

"What's Prince Matchabe up to this year?"

"It irritates me when the corpse doesn't have any visible injuries at all."

"...ut it isn't _supposed_ to make sense!"

"I'm _glad_ we're sending help to Russia now that
they've thanked us."

"Of course, I wouldn't want a card that says _too_ much."

"But does Westchester _want_ a strong Yugoslavia?"

"I know who she'd be crazy about — that little Mitchell dog up in Scarsdale."

Why, Stalin has a dimple! I never noticed it before."

"Go away. You're
rattling me."

"Do you mind if we sing just <u>one</u> Smith song?"

"Now don't let me
speak another word of English!"

"But there's not much point
to looking exotic in Englewood."

"Is anybody Alice Pomeroy, Swarthmore, 1913?"

"Mrs. Brown acts so harassed lately. Do you suppose she's finally found a maid?"

"We've decided to allow our canary to become a mothe

"Have you any _serious_ ashtrays?"

"If everything has a funny taste, don't worry. It's just herbs."

"Guess what Victoria said today —
she said 'please.'"

Helen E. Hokinson

"Of course, they're just at the awkward age

"Perhaps if Madam would try
to meet it halfway . . ."

"Tonight I think I'll go to bed before the murder."

"Surely you can't have misplaced the
Eighteenth Armored Division _again_, Miss MacEldowny!"

"Elizabeth Connor McMeekin, '15?"

"Present. After graduation, I started to take an M.A. at Teachers College, but gave it up to marry Roy McMeekin, Cornell, '12. My husband was only a plant engineer with the telephone company at the time and had not yet become an executive. We lived in Columbus, Ohio, until 1927, when Mr. McMeekin was called to New York, and we built a home in Westchester. I have two children, a girl, Elsie, aged nineteen, and a boy, Donald, aged seventeen. I want to say that I think this Alpha Delta Alpha alumnae picnic is a wonderful idea and that Penny Trowbridge should be congratulated on getting it up. I hope we can get together next summer and repeat it with all the same people."

"It isn't that Macy's *dislikes* Gimbel's, it's just that Macy's prefers
upholster its chairs with its own fabrics."

"New Canaan isn't *really* in
the country. It only *looks* like the country."

"Norman, let's start talking about Christmas."

"Oh, I always send condolences — providing I've <u>known</u> the dog."

"I'm sorry, but I am murdering Mr. Hodgson to the best of my ability!"

"I know what! Let's have an Old-Fashioned before we start talking French."

"...here aren't any bulls who would object to my blouse, are there?"

"Let the birthday girl go first!"

"Now, remember. Pretend you _hate_ Staffordshire!"

"I'm going to be here for only two weeks, and I want clams, clams, clams!"

"..t, Colonel, when you say ..t life as we know it in ..stchester is doomed, surely ..u mean it _humorously_?"

"Well, the truth is,
I'm lukewarm about insane asylums."

"*A very dear friend gave me some wonderful old Scotch, and there just happened to be a bottle of papaya juice in the icebox.*"

"...afraid this is goodbye, Miss MacDonald. I'm joining the Book-of-the-Month Club."

"Mr. Dodd and I just want you to cook very simple meals, do a little dusting and bed-making, and be *happy*."

"Do try to appear calm and matter-of-fact. First impressions are very important."

"I wonder if I could enlist your coöperation in a little scheme I have for livening up my husband."

that's what that Mr. Smith does. I never realized
he didn't have to earn a living."

"Let's try a sixteen and see what happens."

Helen E. Hokinson

"On what floor do I find the hats for better women?"

"Personally, I think Madam looks better in the palm trees than in the wild geese."

"My husband has very definite ideas. He doesn't want me
to look like a mushroom or a rabbit."

"The treasurer wants me to announce that unless some of the members pay
their back dues, she will simply lose her mind."

"What are the __women__ of distinction drinking?"

"I've put you next to a man who may or may not be dangerous."

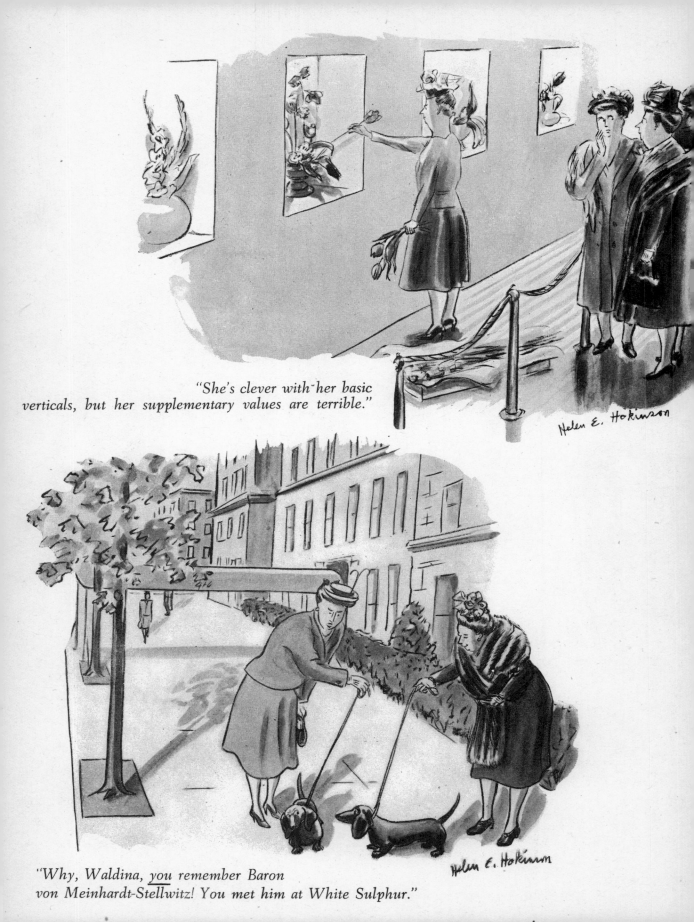

"She's clever with her basic verticals, but her supplementary values are terrible."

Helen E. Hokinson

"Why, Waldina, you remember Baron von Meinhardt-Stellwitz! You met him at White Sulphur."

Helen E. Hokinson

"...ankly, I've reached the stage where I don't care whether stripes are vertical or not."

"Let's try the Débutante Department, just on a wild gamble."

"Of course, you understand these measurements are only temporary."

don't know, I sort of hate to waste a facial on the New Friends of Music."

"Goodness! Isn't Chile thin!"

"Gabriel Heatter was every bit as surprised as I was."

"...ll me, Admiral,
...ich is your favorite ocean?"

"...u want the works, I suppose."

"How can I persuade some very undesirable starlings to move?"

"You mean I can buy some bonds from you sitting right here on this sofa?"

"Madam is really very nice
when she's all together."

"After hearing Colonel Morgan, I'm sure all of us have overcome
any fear we may have had of Japan."

"I insist! After all, summoning four ghosts
from the past was _my_ idea."

"Why, yes, Mr. Stimson did call you a few days ago and wanted you to call him back, but I forgot to tell you because of some trouble I was having with a tooth."

"Would you sanction a tôle breadbasket as a container for portulaca?"

"I just love doing this — it takes my mind off the war."

"A strange woman is sitting in our corner of the porch."

"How can seven people have fun?"

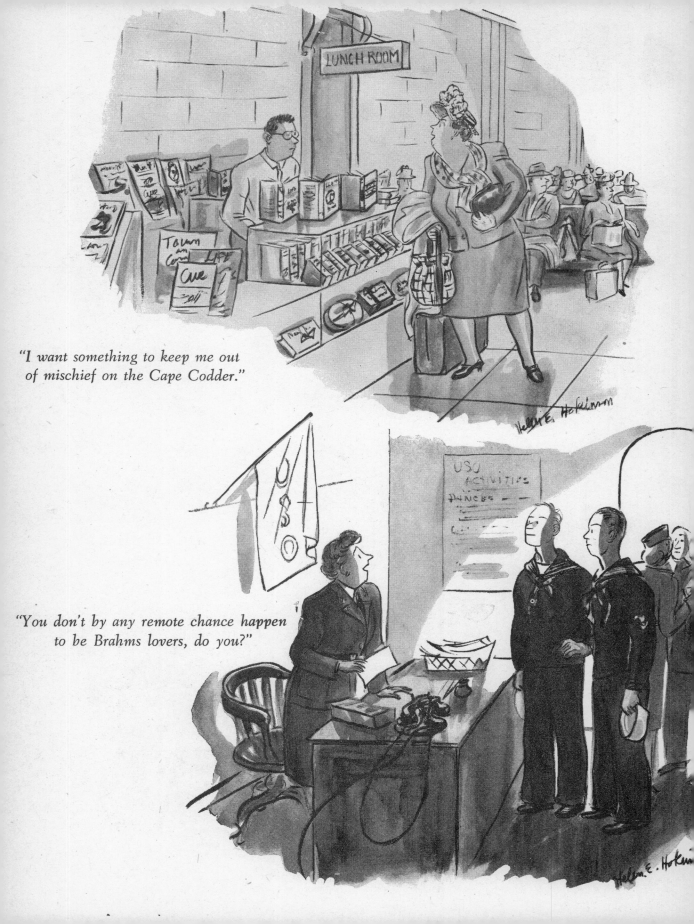

"I want something to keep me out of mischief on the Cape Codder."

"You don't by any remote chance happen to be Brahms lovers, do you?"

"I'm still not satisfied with anyone's kisses!"

wouldn't want to go to Trinidad unless you're sure there'd be somebody else there."

"We're the Eight Reckless Bidders and we have a reservation."

"I've lost a little hat shop."

"Is everybody ready for the Venezuelan national drink?"

"Oh, dear, I hope Consolidated Edison
hasn't done something foolish!"

"They're terribly strict in here about soliciting. You can set your can on the table, but they won't let you shake it."

"Herbert, why can't _we_ collect a little painter who'll be good someday?"

"I feel sorry for Mississippi, but I just don't like to read about it"

Helen E. Hokinson

"Would you mind taking in two drowned rats?"

"This won't change my thinking, will it?"

"Haven't you got something I could just squeeze or push?"

"Oh dear!"

"It's to pour over grapefruit."

"I really expected to look a little different for twenty-eight dollars."

"George, why don't we ever go to places like Cartier's and just look around?"

"Now, please bear in mind that I am *not* Ingrid Bergman."

and this one means that you beseech the sun god to ripen the corn."

"Why is this cigar any better than that cigar?"

Helen E. Hokinson

"Right after church we're going to try hot buttered rum made with oleo."

"Before I introduce Mr. Garrison, I ought to mention something. He's had I don't know _how_ many wives, but it wasn't his fault."

"Oh, did I tell you about the perfectly lovely compliment a saleswoman in Bonwit's coat department paid me this afternoon?"

"There's something I want to ask you, Colonel. Would the Army like to know how to make Spam interesting?"

"I don't know how everybody else feels, but _I_ feel like weeding."

"I'll tell you one thing — Henry James wasn't <u>worth</u> a forty-seven-cent fine."

"Well, of course a <u>good</u> sex maniac is always hard to find."

"Harvey, do you <u>really</u> like the Dodgers, or is it just a pose?"

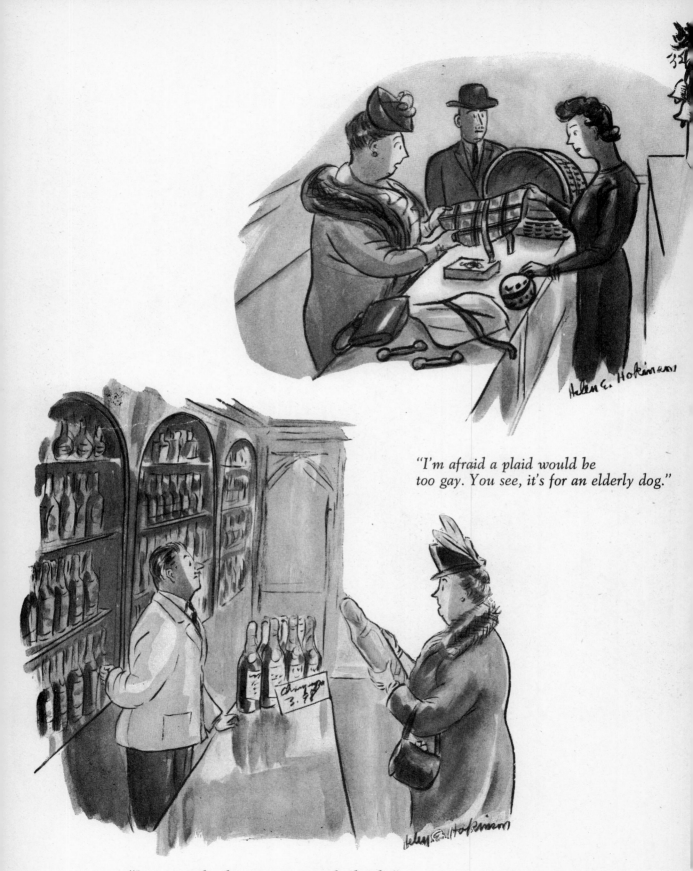

"I'm afraid a plaid would be too gay. You see, it's for an elderly dog."

"I suppose the directions are on the bottle."

"I don't mind the American Revolution as long as it doesn't have too much sex in it."

"What do you think, George! You're giving me something for Christmas that you won't have to pay for all at once."

"The taxis are pretending they don't see me."

"If there are any of those deductions I'm not entitled to, don't hesitate to say so."

"Which is the vitamin
that takes the place of Florida?"

"Which do _you_ think is more Christmasy?
Tammany Hall one hundred years ago or a
panda?"

"It overwhelmed Brooks Atkinson, but it isn't overwhelming me."

"We want to send a hostess present to a dachshund."

". . . and then I covered them with dirt, and that was the last I ever saw of them."

"*Martha, I hope you're going to be as thrilled by this news as I am. I've just inherited a farm!*"

"*My husband is going to be the most surprised man in Plainfield.*"

"If you should happen to be in Plummer's at any time, Mr. Robinson on the second floor knows what I want for Christmas."

"Isn't it about time another one of John Gunther's 'Insides' came out?"

"My red spiders liked your rotenone dust!"

"I don't really like Bach, but I respect him."